C000108176

STOPPING SMOKING

A SURVIVAL GUIDE

BY MARTIN BAXENDALE

ISBN 0-9539303-1-9

Printed in England by Stoate & Bishop Printers Ltd,
The Runnings, Cheltenham, Glos. GL51 9NH.

Webb site: www.silentbutdeadly.co.uk

CONTENTS

INTRODUCTION

After almost 25 years of smoking twenty or more a day, I finally quit seven years ago after a number of failed attempts. So I know what it's like to try to stop, and it isn't easy.

But you can vastly increase your chances of success if you plan and prepare for it, rather than simply saying "okay, I'll stop today" with no preparation or planning at all.

I hope the following pages will not only give you a good laugh but also encourage you to have a go (or have another go if you've tried before) at quitting, and to keep on trying until you succeed.

It takes a lot of effort, but it really is worth it. Good luck.

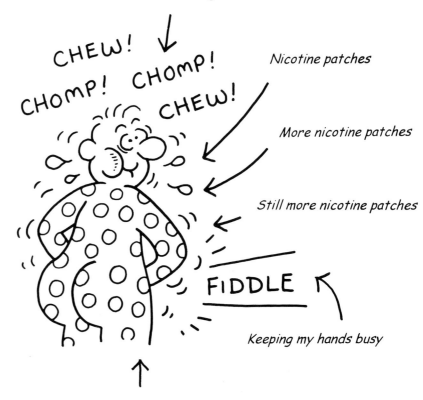

Mouth stuffed with nicotine gum

CHEW! CHOMP! CHOMP! CHEW!

Nicotine patches

More nicotine patches

Still more nicotine patches

FIDDLE

Keeping my hands busy

ME TRYING TO STOP SMOKING

ME <u>BEFORE</u> I STOPPED SMOKING

ME <u>AFTER</u> I STOPPED SMOKING

Smelly hair

Smoker's cough

Unhealthy spotty skin

Wheezy chest

Smelly fag-breath

COUGH!

WHEEZE!

EMPTY

Smelly clothes

No spare cash (All spent on ciggies).

Gas mask

Air-freshener

Sweet-smelling

Glowing with good health

Loads of spare dosh

ME _BEFORE_ I STOPPED SMOKING

↓

SORRY! I'LL HAVE TO STOP AGAIN TO GET MY BREATH BACK!

COUGH!
COUGH!
PUFF!
SNORE!
GASP!
WHEEZE!
... PANT!

ME _AFTER_ I STOPPED SMOKING

↓

I'LL BE HOME IN TWO MINUTES DARLING! PUT YOUR SEXY UNDIES ON AND GET OUT THE TRAMPOLINE!

Packet of 500

Just finishing 20-mile daily run (including quick stop at chemist's)

EDITOR'S NOTE: The publishers would like to apologize for the author's obsession with his supposedly increased sexual appeal and performance since stopping smoking. He may not smell like a bonfire any more or get out of breath just climbing the stairs to the bedroom, but he's still an ugly bugger with a tiny willy!

PREPARING TO STOP

First of all, are you sure you really do <u>want</u> to stop smoking? Going into it half-heartedly won't exactly increase your chances of success.

It will help to strengthen your resolve if you first take some time to think about your reasons for stopping, maybe discuss them with someone else or even make a written list to remind you why you're doing this if you start to waver later on.

Top of the list should of course be your health, and "the damage is already done" should never be an excuse to carry on smoking. The human body has an amazing capacity for self-repair and no matter how long you've been smoking, your health should start improving almost from the moment you stop, and the longer you stay stopped, the more the risk of serious smoking-related diseases decreases.

7

REASONS FOR STOPPING:

Tick off those that apply to you, and add any others that you can think of.

☐ I'm concerned about my health.

☐ I want to feel better, more energetic and less tired.

☐ I want to look better (clearer skin, better complexion).

☐ It's a dirty, smelly habit.

☐ I hate wasting my money.

☐ I don't want to encourage my children to start smoking.

☐ I hate being hooked on nicotine.

....

....

Reasons for stopping No. 23: I'm fed up with having to re-paint all the nicotine-stained ceilings every bloody year!

ASK FOR SUPPORT: Tell friends, family and colleagues that you're going to stop smoking and ask them to help you by being supportive and encouraging, being understanding if you're irritable, helping you to keep busy and not think about smoking, avoiding smoking in front of you, not offering you cigarettes, etc.

PLAN AHEAD: Plan activities to keep you busy and take your mind off cigarettes, especially in the first few days; such as DIY jobs around the house, gardening, sports, outings, trips, walks etc.

And aim to avoid as much as possible those situations where you know you are most likely to be tempted to start smoking again; like pubs and bars, boozy parties and anywhere that you know people are likely to be smoking.

It doesn't have to be forever. As time goes on and you beat the habit and the craving for cigarettes, you'll feel less and less tempted to start again even in the most difficult situations. But in the first few days and weeks you really do need to go out of your way to make things easier on yourself.

Redecorating is one way of keeping busy when you're trying to stop smoking, and will also freshen-up your smoky house or flat.

LICK!

STOP LICKING THE NICOTINE OFF THE CEILING!

"CUTTING DOWN": It's not a good idea to try stopping smoking by cutting down gradually. You'll only prolong the agony for yourself and end up constantly thinking about your next cigarette, how many you're allowed, and so on.

What you should be aiming for is to try to forget about cigarettes completely, stop thinking about them, stop them being a part of your life.

If you can stop completely and stay stopped long enough, you will eventually reach the stage where you don't think about cigarettes at all, where they simply aren't important to you any more, where you are finally a non-smoker.

And the quickest way to reach that stage is to stop smoking completely from the very start. Anything else can only drag out the whole process.

I'M CUTTING DOWN! LAST YEAR I WAS ON TWENTY A DAY, AND THIS YEAR I'M ON NINETEEN A DAY!

PLAN REWARDS: You should plan regular treats to reward yourself for not smoking, especially in the early stages; little presents to yourself, a special meal, eating out, a good bottle of wine, flowers, a relaxing sauna or massage, etc.

And perhaps your family and/or your partner could also arrange regular little treats and rewards, to mark each week and month that you stay a non-smoker and help encourage you to keep it up.

However, take care not to go overboard on high-calorie treats like chocolate if you're concerned about possible weight gain as a side-effect of quitting (**see also pages 25-26**).

MARTIN BAXENDALE'S "HANDY STOPPING SMOKING HINT" No. 1:

You can make up your own book of 'Not-Smoking' reward vouchers to tear out and exchange with your partner for regular little treats as long as you continue not to smoke; e.g. a special meal, a massage, or "I promise to ....your..............all evening/morning if you haven't smoked for a week, and I won't complain that my.............is getting tired" (fill in the gaps to suit your particular choice of depraved sexual activity).

CHOOSE A DAY: Try to decide when would be a good time to stop. Would a weekend or during a holiday period be best, or while you're working? It may well depend on when you normally smoke most; at home or at work, when relaxing or when under stress.

Then choose a day and stick to it. And the day before you start to quit, make sure you get rid of all your smoking paraphernalia; not just your cigarettes, cigars, or tobacco, but also any cigarette lighters, papers, pipes, and even ashtrays.

And don't just put your cigarettes away in a drawer. If you have any left, get rid of them completely or they'll inevitably turn into a tormenting temptation later on.

MARTIN BAXENDALE'S "HANDY STOPPING SMOKING HINT" No. 2:

...99...100! READY OR NOT, I'M COMING TO FIND YOU!

X WRONG!
Don't just hide your last half-smoked packet of cigarettes. →

IT'S ONLY A BIT OF CURRY SAUCE! IT'LL DRY OUT ON THE RADIATOR!

X WRONG!
Don't bin cigarettes intact either. Destroy them!

X WRONG!

If burning your last left-over ciggies, beware the temptation to stick your head in the fireplace for one last huge lungful of smoke as they go up in flames.

✓ RIGHT!

I would strongly recommend the following: Minimize the likelihood of your attempting to retrieve discarded cigarettes for a sneaky smoke later on by shredding in a food blender at high speed for five minutes, then thoroughly mixing with kitty litter in the cat tray.

STOPPING AND STAYING STOPPED

AIDS TO STOPPING:

Nicotine gum or patches can be useful as a temporary aid to help break the smoking habit.

If you can manage without them, so much the better. But smoking <u>is</u> both a habit and an addiction, and in my case I found it easier to break the habit first and then the addiction by weaning myself off cigarettes with nicotine gum and then gradually replacing that with chewing gum.

And if you want something to chew or suck frequently as a cigarette substitute, other than nicotine gum, sugar-free chewing gum, sweets and lollies (available from chemists) are a better choice than the normal sugary varieties, especially if you're concerned about putting on weight when you stop smoking.

MARTIN BAXENDALE'S "HANDY STOPPING SMOKING HINT" No. 3:

Nicotine gums and patches are rather expensive, but don't be tempted to save money by making your own DIY versions at home.

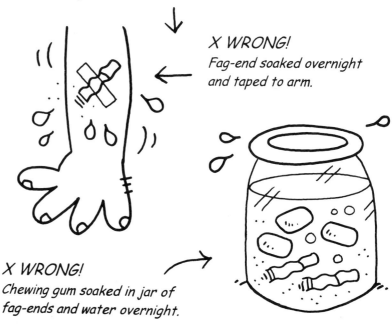

X WRONG!
Fag-end soaked overnight and taped to arm.

X WRONG!
Chewing gum soaked in jar of fag-ends and water overnight.

Hypnotherapy may help to bolster your determination to stop smoking by getting you to concentrate on positive thoughts like "I don't want a cigarette" instead of constantly dwelling on the fact that you want to smoke but can't.

And there are various relaxation techniques you can try like yoga and t'ai chi (books and evening courses are widely available) to help reduce stress and take your mind of the cravings.

In fact anything that relaxes you will help, including herbal remedies, massages, saunas, aromatherapy, even just a long soak in a warm bath.

Regular exercise is also good for countering the stress of stopping smoking, making your body produce lots of endorphins, the chemicals which give you a natural 'high' and make you feel good after a run or a work-out.

Some people find that hypnotherapy helps.

CHANGING YOUR HABITS:

You may find that in the first days and weeks you need to change your habits to avoid situations that you associate with smoking and which will make your cravings worse.

Try to avoid pubs and bars for a while, and generally take care with alcohol as many people feel especially tempted to start smoking again after they've had a few drinks.

If you usually smoke a cigarette with your tea or coffee, try drinking juice or mineral water instead.

And if you tend to have a cigarette after meals, try going for a walk instead of sitting around after you've eaten or settling in front of the TV straight away.

MARTIN BAXENDALE'S "HANDY STOPPING SMOKING HINT" No. 4:

Gas mask, so you can't smell the smoke.

Dark smoked-glass eye-pieces so you can't see the cigarettes in people's mouths so clearly.

Ear-plugs, so you don't have to listen to smokers inhaling.

Baseball bat, for hitting people who think it's funny to offer you ciggies and blow smoke at you even though they know you're trying to quit.

RECOMMENDED SURVIVAL KIT FOR ASSOCIATING WITH PEOPLE WHO SMOKE (E.G. DOWN THE PUB, AT PARTIES, ETC) WHEN YOU'RE TRYING TO STOP.

Try also, in the first days and weeks, to avoid hanging around with friends who smoke or where you know there are likely to be people smoking (e.g. a rest area or designated smoking area at work).

Otherwise your chances of starting smoking again will skyrocket as you're constantly surrounded by temptation (and even smoking "friends" actually offering you cigarettes even though they know you're trying to stop!)

MARTIN BAXENDALE'S "HANDY STOPPING SMOKING HINT" No.5:

Beware the temptation to hang around people who smoke, attracted by the smell of their cigarettes. You could end up an habitual <u>secondary smoker</u>!

SUCK!

SUCK!

↑ VROOOM!

Portable battery-operated vacuum cleaner.

Saving some smoke for later. ↗

17

KEEP YOUR HANDS BUSY:

You'll probably find you miss having a cigarette between your fingers and the habitual hand-to-mouth motions, especially if you were a heavy smoker.

If so, find something else to fiddle with and/or put in your mouth; such as a pen, pencil, sugar-free lollipop, etc.

MARTIN BAXENDALE'S "HANDY STOPPING SMOKING HINT" No. 6:

KEEPING YOUR HANDS BUSY.

X WRONG!

Strangling people who annoy you when you're feeling irritable from not smoking.

STRANGLE!

GLURK!

X WRONG!

Fiddling with yourself in public.

FIDDLE!

✓ RIGHT!

Squeezey stress-relief ball.

Pen or pencil.

TWIDDLE!

SMOKE-FREE ZONES:

Try to create smoke-free zones at home and work, at least to start with, to make it easier for you to stay stopped.

If smoking is permitted at your workplace, tell colleagues that you're trying to stop and ask if they'll avoid smoking where you have to work, maybe going outside instead, or smoking only in one designated area.

If anyone else smokes at home, ask them if they'd mind helping you by smoking outside and not indoors, and do the same with visitors who smoke.

MARTIN BAXENDALE'S "HANDY STOPPING SMOKING HINT" No. 7:

NO SMOKING

DRIP!

DRIP!

DRIP!

TRY TO MAKE YOUR HOME A SMOKE-FREE ZONE.

19

WATCHING TELEVISION:

If you're trying to quit, it can be an added temptation to watch people smoking on television, especially in old films where actors will often make a great show of smoking cigarettes with huge enjoyment or with incredible style and flair!

Before cinemas became largely non-smoking, it was a widely recognized phenomenon that when an actor on the screen lit up, so did large numbers of the audience.

If you find it's getting to you, switch channels for a while or go and get a drink or a snack, have a pee break or whatever. It sounds like a small thing, but you don't need <u>any</u> added pressure when you're trying to quit, no matter how small.

"JUST ONE WON'T HURT":

It's all too easy to give in to the temptation to "just have one". After all, it isn't really <u>starting</u> again.

But it is, and every time you do it, you'll put yourself back where you began, psychologically giving in and (if you've managed to get over the nicotine addiction) potentially starting the nicotine cravings all over again.

Hire an ex-SAS sniper or Mafia hit-man to follow you around and, if you try to light up, shoot the cigarette out of your mouth from a nearby roof-top.

Note: If you can't afford an expert sniper, and have to make do with the local poacher or amateur gun-nut, be sure to wear a helmet and body-armour at all times.

MARTIN BAXENDALE'S "HANDY STOPPING SMOKING HINT" No. 8:

MARTIN BAXENDALE'S "HANDY STOPPING SMOKING HINT" No. 9:

This simple device will help to stop you lighting-up for a sneaky smoke when you're supposed to be trying to stop.

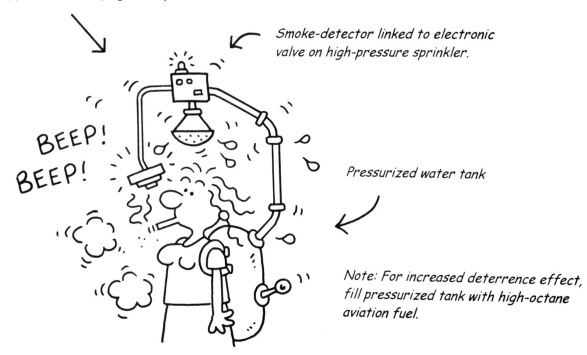

Smoke-detector linked to electronic valve on high-pressure sprinkler.

BEEP! BEEP!

Pressurized water tank

Note: For increased deterrence effect, fill pressurized tank with high-octane aviation fuel.

SAVE YOUR CIGARETTE MONEY:

Try to save-up the money you would have spent on smoking, while you're quitting, so you can spend it on a big treat when you've managed to stay stopped for a good long time.

After a few months you may well find, especially if you were a heavy smoker, that you've saved enough for a holiday or at least a nice weekend break somewhere special.

IF WE'D BEEN SMOKING 30 A DAY, WE COULD HAVE SAVED ENOUGH FOR TWO WEEKS IN MAJORCA INSTEAD OF JUST ONE!

PUTTING ON WEIGHT:

I've heard smokers say that they can't stop because they always gain a lot of weight when they try. But continuing to smoke and ruining your health isn't exactly the best way to control your weight!

You may well find that you do want to eat more when you quit, as smoking can act as an appetite suppressor. But if you eat sensibly and get a little more exercise, that doesn't have to mean that you'll pile on the pounds.

Try to avoid eating too many fatty and sugary foods, especially in the early days when the cigarette cravings are strongest and most likely to push you into over-eating.

And try not to use high-calorie snack foods, sweets, chocolate, and sugary fizzy drinks as comforting cigarette substitutes to help get you through the day. Much better to eat some fresh fruit or raw vegetable sticks if you need to snack between meals.

X WRONG!

Peanuts

MUNCH!

Cola

Doughnuts

Crisps

Sweets

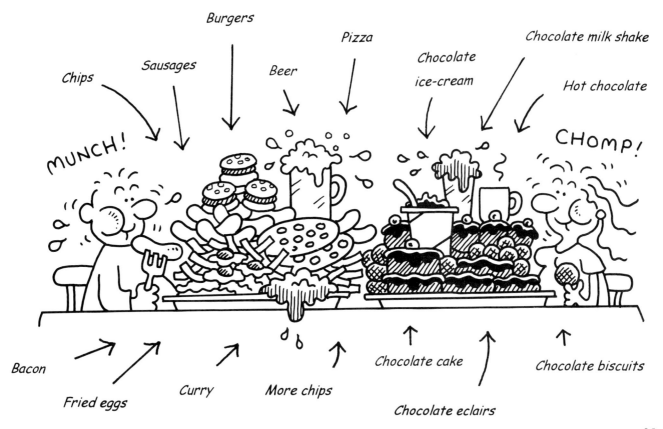

Remember also to take care with alcohol. Heavy drinking is not only likely to make you more prone to starting smoking again when you've had a few, but there are a heck of a lot of calories in booze, which can seriously add to potential weight-gain problems, especially in combination with high-fat foods and snacks.

And don't forget that a little extra exercise can go a long way towards keeping your weight down if you do start to eat more. Just a simple walk after a meal, an occasional swim, or taking up a new sport can make a real difference.

REGULAR EXERCISE WILL HELP REDUCE WEIGHT-GAIN.

X WRONG!

Weight-lifting down the pub every night.

✓ RIGHT!

Swimming is very good exercise, and it's difficult to light-up a sneaky ciggy in the pool.

GETTING IRRITABLE

Just about every smoker who tries to stop tends to get much more irritable and short-tempered than usual in the first days and weeks.

And that's not much fun for the people around you, who may be doing their best to support you and help you to stay stopped only to have your irritation taken out on them day in and day out.

So try to be aware of your behaviour towards others and not treat them with unreasonable snappiness.

Warn friends, family and work colleagues that you're going to stop smoking, so that they'll know to tread softly around you for a while and hopefully make some allowances for you if you do get snappy with them. Trying to relax more (see page 15) will help, as will cutting down on alcohol **and coffee and exercising more.**

I QUIT SMOKING YESTERDAY, SO DON'T GET ME ANNOYED, YOU F***ING LITTLE SH*T !!

Warn friends, family and work colleagues that you're going to stop smoking, so that they'll understand if you get snappy and irritable.

27

MARTIN BAXENDALE'S "HANDY STOPPING SMOKING HINT" No. 10:

YOUR PERSONAL BAD-TEMPER SURVIVAL KIT FOR WHEN YOU GET IRRITABLE AND RATTY WHILE YOU'RE STOPPING SMOKING.

Ear defenders to protect your ears from the noise of you constantly slamming doors bad-temperedly behind you.

Throat pastilles and soothing gargle for when your throat gets sore from shouting at people (and inanimate objects) that get on your nerves and annoy you when you're trying to stop smoking.

Soothing bruise cream for when your knuckles and forehead get sore from punching and nutting people (and inanimate objects) that annoy you.

Steel-toe-capped boots to protect your toes from repeated kicking of inanimate objects that annoy you.

MARTIN BAXENDALE'S "HANDY STOPPING SMOKING HINT" No. 11:

BAD-TEMPER DECOY FOR USE AT HOME.

Decoy dummies of family members/partner/ friends/relatives. Keep in garage, shed or spare room, for taking your bad-temper out on when you're irritable and ratty while trying to stop smoking.

Will save wear-and-tear on your <u>real</u> family, friends and relations and help to ensure that you end up a non-smoker <u>and</u> with people still talking to you.

MARTIN BAXENDALE'S "HANDY STOPPING SMOKING HINT" No. 12:

BAD-TEMPER DECOY FOR USE BEFORE WORK.

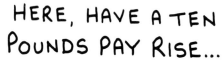

HERE, HAVE A TEN POUNDS PAY RISE...

TEN POUNDS?!! YOU OLD SKINFLINT.!!

Tape recorder.

Decoy dummy of boss/work colleague, for you to take your temper out on before you go to work, if you're feeling very irritable while stopping smoking.

Will get at least _some_ of the rattiness out of your system so you're not so snappy with people when you get to work.